MW00587356

Same Elephants

THE HUMAN OATH

We are humans
From all around the world
One kind only
And that is humankind

Marjy Marj

Same Elephants

Same Elephants

Dear Reader,

Thanks for deciding to check out my writing. This book is possible because of the friendships that I have built along the way.

I owe a debt of gratitude to my family and friends.

Because of you, I have learned that although we may have our differences, at the end of the day, we are all humans.

I hope that through this work of fiction, we will all learn to be tolerant of others.

Dig in, enjoy and let your imagination take you on a human adventure!

Same Elephants

SAME ELEPHANTS

MARJY MARJ

Same Elephants

Triple A Press
A3

Same Elephants

For my girlfriends - Together, we are powerful

This book is dedicated to my sweet Sallybaby.
I love you Mama!
Elephant you, Elephant me!

Same Elephants

Acknowledgements

There are so many people who helped bring this book to life. I thank you all from the bottom of my heart.

First, I'd like to thank Rob Williams for working with me to create a beautiful and vibrant cover for this book.

I'd also like to give a special shout out to Esther Bodek, Masha Temkin, Lilla Marie Williamson and Meimuna Bamba, the inspiration behind Same Elephants. I'm so blessed to have met and broken bread with you.

To Morkor Newman, thanks for your help with the research process.

Bethany Cobb and Lee Healy, thanks for your comments during the cover production phase of the book. You guys are hard critics!

To Mary Thomas, Hope Logan, Erika McJimpsey, Araceli Hernandez-Laroche, Loreta Dylgjeri, Carter Graves, Sam Mitchell, Misti Hudson, Evelyn Boateng and Dorothy Sangmuah - Thank you for the valuable lessons.

Most of all, thanks to Boss Kofi and Adom for being my sounding boards - It's all good!

NOTE

This is a work of fiction.

See back pages for glossary.

Same Elephants

MEET THE GIRLS

Jane Taylor

Jane is a fiesty journalist. An activist and advocate for human rights, she is always ready to offer a helping hand to her friends. Jane does not believe in deities.

Rakiya Muhammad

Rakiya is a second year family medicine resident. She's been working on her chief resident speech for the past 2 months. If she wins the election, she will be the first African American female chief resident for the Med South program. She loves politics and hopes to run for office some day.

Aviva Schwartz

Aviva is a brilliant investment banker. Despite her wealthy background, she is humble and hardworking. She is excited about her upcoming wedding. She can't believe she's about to marry Asher. Her eyes glisten with happy tears.

Sasha Badu

That's me. I am a black immigrant girl originally from Ghana, West Africa. I was brought to America as a maid when I was 13 years old. I can't believe I have the opportunity to fly to Maui for my friend's wedding. From Ash Town to Yankey. I'm feeling myself.

Same Elephants

CURRENT SITUATION

PART I - REMINISCE

PART II - NEXT CHAPTER

Same Elephants

CURRENT SITUATION

LIFE

Chai, this Yankey. I'm still here.

I thought life was going to be much better but it looks like money comes, money goes is my current situation.

My paddies are doing well though. Why won't they? They don't have the additional responsibilities that I'm saddled with.

In addition to my living expenses, I have to send money to Ash Town every month. Taking care of my parents and siblings is no joke. School fees, books, food... Charlay, it's not easy.

Although my banking job is decent, I wish I could find a higher paying job.

The job market is tough. And it doesn't help that I have a weird name on my resume. Maybe an American name would have helped open more doors.

Sometimes when the recruiters speak to me over the phone, they think I'm British. But then when I show up for the interview they realize that I'm black.

That's when they come up with all these excuses about why they can't hire me for the position. The sad part is that they turn around and hire candidates who are less qualified for the job.

Chai! This Yankey life is full of ups and downs. Curveball after curveball.

One day that suburban house with the two car garage will happen. I have faith.

Same Elephants

PART I

REMINISCE

Same Elephants

PAPER

Same Elephants

PAPER

God is good! All the time!

As I held the green card in my hands, I grinned from ear to ear. It was real! The conditions had been removed. Finally!

No more worrying about deportation.

The green card was a coveted prize in my community. There was not a single revival that a Pastor did not talk about people's green card situations.

You would have thought that having that card was the answer to all of one's problems.

I was delighted. The application process had been stressful and arduous.

When Lamar and I got married, I thought the permanent residence application process was going to be simple.

He was going to file for me. I would be approved for a green card. And then we would live happily ever after.

Oh, how I was wrong.

I hadn't anticipated the marriage wahala.

The cheating, drinking, beating...

I just couldn't stay in that apartment with him.

Moving out was the best decision.

But then I had to strategize for that card.

The United States Custom and Immigration Services was not going to remove the conditions on my green card just because I was married to an American.

I had to make some hard decisions.

I'm glad it all worked out. I was finally a green card holder. As my family would say, I had paper.

This was a milestone in my life and I had to celebrate.

But before heading out for the celebration, I placed that phone call to Mama in Kumasi.

The call was probably one of the best conversations she had had with me since I came to America.

I could hear the elation and relief in her voice. The family had been praying and fasting throughout the interview process.

My success was theirs.

If a green card could land me a better job with more money, they were all for it.

Mama couldn't believe that her daughter had papers in America.

I'm sure the whole neighborhood heard about our good news that evening!

Same Elephants

THE ROAD TO BACHELORS

Same Elephants

THE ROAD TO BACHELORS

Having the green card was a confidence booster for me.

I was more excited about applying to a 4 year college.

With an Associate Degree in Business Administration from Montgomery Community College in my 'pocket', I was ready for the next step.

The application process was easy. It was the wait process that got to me.

I was hoping to transfer into a local college because I thought it was going to be easier to find money for in-state tuition.

My caution did not deter me from applying to a few out of town colleges that were willing to accept the credits from my Associate Degree.

I really wanted to enroll as a junior. I didn't want to end up paying for more than 2 additional years of college.

However, the process was more difficult than I anticipated. Despite having great test scores and a high enough GPA, my transfer wasn't a shoo-in.
While some colleges would accept me if I was willing to enroll as a sophomore, some of the schools had high rejection rates for community college transfer students.

With the kind of responses that I was receiving from the schools, I began losing hope.

Although a school like the University of Maryland, was high on my list, I'd given up on the possibility of enrolling in such a fine institution.

It was much harder to enroll as a transfer student at the in-state top tier schools.

To my surprise, my first 'acceptance' letter came from the University of Maryland.

I was thrilled!

As soon as I found out, I committed to attending. I was no longer interested in the other schools.

In August of 1994, I walked into the University of Maryland College Park classrooms with pride!

From a village girl to a college girl.

Yes, that was me! I had come far.

I counted myself fortunate.

The future looked bright.

Although the financial aid package from Maryland did not cover my full tuition, the student loans and my measly paycheck helped me cover expenses.

Truthfully, I don't know what I would have done if I hadn't qualified for financial aid and loans.

I was proud to be enrolled as an International Business major at the Robert H. Smith School of Business.

Having legal papers had helped open doors for me.

Same Elephants

A CHANCE MEETING

Same Elephants

A CHANCE MEETING

It didn't take long to settle into the flow of being a student again. The campus was always buzzing with students and activities. Although I had to work 30 hours a week, I still tried to fit a few on-campus events into my schedule.

Most of the events that I chose to attend involved free food. This student was all about saving money.

The free food events ranged from student club meetings, sororities, speaker series, lunch and learns, workshops to political seminars.

1994 being a gubernatorial election year in Maryland, there were lots of political events on campus.

It didn't matter if it was a Glendening or Sauerbrey event, you were bound to find me there.

I could belong to any political party that would feed me.

One late afternoon, as I walked through campus, I saw a flyer advertising a Democrats for Sauerbrey event. As usual, the ad included free pizza.

As a hungry college student, I decided to head to the event. Fortunately, the meeting was being held at the Van Munching Hall which was about 10 minutes away.

At the doorway, a girl with a hijab welcomed me and asked me to sign in by providing my email address. I really didn't want to leave my real address but I did anyway. This way, I could find out about more free stuff in the future.

When I entered the room, I wasn't really interested in listening to the rhetoric. I headed to the food table, grabbed 2 slices of pizza and was in the process of taking the last can of sprite when an obnoxious girl came out of nowhere to pick that sprite.

I gave her a side eye but didn't confront her because I didn't want to fight with a white girl. I just didn't want anybody to label me as an angry black girl.

I walked to one of the corner tables to finish my pizza. I didn't want to make it too obvious that I was just there for the food.

It was an interesting discussion.

The Republican representatives explained the importance of voting for Sauerbrey and her policies.

They talked about how she was paving the way for women.

I could be down with that, I thought.

As a fan of Glendening, I wondered if I should give Sauerbrey a chance. It sounded like she wasn't a bad candidate.

Sitting in the room, looking at the demographics, I wondered why the girl in the hijab was part of a group organizing an event for Sauerbrey.

I thought it was weird that a black muslim would be supporting a Republican event.

Ah well, who was I to judge anyone?

I mean, the only reason I decided to patronize the event was because of the food. Like me, she may have had her reasons.

I turned my attention back to the speaker.

As I swallowed the last drops of water, the last speaker wrapped up the discussion and thanked everyone for attending.

Mission accomplished. I had secured a free meal before class.

I picked up my backpack and started making my way to the door.

Across the room, I saw the white girl who took the soda. It seemed like she was smiling at me.

I couldn't be bothered.
Why was she fake smiling at me?
Then she started waving and walking toward me.

I decided that I was going to play nice. It didn't matter that she had outsmarted me earlier.

She grinned and introduced herself.

Her name was Jane. Like me, she was a junior. She apologized for taking the last soda and offered to hang out sometime. The girl standing next to Jane nodded in agreement. I figured they were friends.

I was surprised. Why did she want to hang out with me? She didn't know me? Or even know anything about me.

Mind you, I didn't really have friends on campus. I was kind of a loner. I came to class, went to work and then went back home to hang out with my 'cousin' roomie Bambi.

Maybe hanging out with Jane wasn't a bad idea.

Before I could accept the apology or even agree to a hang out, Jane asked if I'd like to go to the John Grisham author event the following week.

She had heard that the food was going to be really good.

Whoa! That was fast. She already had an event in mind?

Chuckle chuckle. Maybe I wasn't the only one scouting for free food events.

I smiled back at her. That wasn't a bad idea.

I actually liked reading Grisham books. I had even started contemplating a legal career after reading 'The Firm'.

But then I asked myself - why would I agree to hang out with these strangers?

Yeah, I wanted to go to the event but did I want to go with these 2?

Ah well. Maybe it'd give me an opportunity to make new friends. Maybe I should consider going to the Grisham event with them?

Wait a minute, I realized that I hadn't even told them my name.

"By the way, I'm Aviva" said Jane's friend.

Lawd, do these girls ever stop talking? I thought.

They wouldn't have guessed what I was thinking because I smiled back at them.

And then I did a small wave.
My name is Sasha, I said.

"Nice to meet you Sasha," they both chimed.

Then they proceeded to tell me how they loved my outfit.

I was wearing an African print skirt.

Again, I smiled and said thank you.

From the look on Aviva's face, I knew she had more to say about my skirt. I started counting 3, 2, 1...

Aviva was right on cue.

She had seen some of those prints during her recent trip to Kenya. She went on to describe how nice the people were. And how they had met some kind guides from the Maasai tribe.

Again, I smiled back and told her that was great.

I omitted to tell them that I had never been to Kenya and did not know anything about the Maasai tribe.

I probably had to find time to go to the library to do some research on African tribes. A lot of people had been asking me about Africa lately.

I wasn't even that familiar with West Africa. I needed to beef up my knowledge on the continent.

Despite making all this small talk, I was yet to confirm my decision to join them for the Grisham event.

I knew I was definitely interested in going.
Maybe it was time for me to hang out with some other students.

I asked for additional details.

Jane handed me a flyer from her backpack.

The information looked good.

Yes, I was going to attend the event with Jane and Aviva.

I felt kind of weird. But hey, I agreed anyway.

We chatted for a little bit.

It seemed like we had a good rapport.

Aviva thought it'd be nice to get coffee or even study together.

That sounded good. But I wasn't going to spend my money on an expensive cup of coffee?

A study group sounded better to me.

That was kind of cool.
I had never been the kind of girl to study with groups back at Montgomery Community College.

Sounded like I was finally connecting with some Maryland students.

Too soon, it was time to head back to class.

Like me, Jane and Aviva had to leave too.
We exchanged phone numbers and promised to catch up later.

Before leaving the room, I decided to go say thank you to the girl in the hijab.

To my surprise, she was very pleasant. She was glad that I had come to the meeting and offered me some political pamphlets.

I wondered if she was a political science major. Maybe she was going to run for office some day. Her name was Rakiya.

Same Elephants

FRIENDS

FRIENDS

It didn't take too long for Jane, Aviva and I to become friends. We started studying and hanging out together.

On the day of the Grisham talk, we decided to meet at Maryland Dairy, an on campus ice cream joint. We weren't really planning on buying ice cream. We just wanted to get together before the event.

Since I finished with class early and had time to spare, I was the first to arrive.

My plan was to just hang around the shop. I was going to try and revise my notes as I waited.

Shortly after I got there, Rakiya walked in. She was excited to see me. She had vouchers for free scoops of ice cream and had decided to use one that day.

She was wondering what I was doing at the shop. I told her I was meeting Jane and Aviva from the other night.

Yeah, she was familiar with Jane and Aviva but they weren't her friends. She thought that Jane was pretty loud. We laughed about that.

Since Rakiya had a few vouchers, she offered me one. I looked at the wall clock and realized that I had some time to kill.

Chocolate ice cream didn't sound like a bad idea, so I decided to use my newly acquired voucher.

It was kind of nice talking to Rakiya. She sounded smart.

And she had the scoop on the professors and student life. She had been at Maryland since her freshman year.

As I listened to Rakiya, I realized that her student experience was different from mine. Living off campus and having an almost full time job while being a student meant that I was only focused on getting in and out of class.

I didn't really have the time to hang out with other students or participate in most on campus activities.

I figured I could learn a lot about the ins and outs of campus life by befriending Rakiya.

I had never attended a college game or campus party. Maybe she and I could go together?

Rakiya sounded genuine and friendly.

When she told me that her friends called her Kiya, I asked if I could call her that too. Of course, she said.

I smiled. I couldn't wait to tell Bambi about my new friend.

As we sat there nibbling on the ice cream, I asked Kiya if she'd want to come to the Grisham event.

For a few seconds, she was quiet.

Her response? She said she would have rather gone to a Maya Angelou or Terry McMillan author event.

Oh? I couldn't fathom why someone who volunteered for on-campus political events wouldn't be interested in an author who wrote legal thrillers.

To me, politics and law went hand in hand.

I just thought that she would have jumped at the opportunity to see and hear John Grisham live.

I was curious about Kiya's reaction so I asked her why she was hesitant about the event.

She smiled. She didn't have anything against the author. She just wished that there was more support for authors of color.

She explained how it was important for her to see herself in books.

As much as she enjoyed reading from diverse authors, she felt that there were not enough mainstream diverse authors.

Although there were several diverse books out there, they just didn't get the attention that they deserved. It seemed that the publishers and book industry were interested in promoting and rewarding white authors.

She thought it was unfair that the minority authors that she liked did not get as much publicity in the mainstream media.

For me, that was eye opening. I hadn't really thought about the book industry in that way. Kiya was making a lot of sense. It was important for people to appreciate the work of people who looked like me.

She began telling me about how important it was, to introduce books written by authors of color in the classroom.

She shared the story about how 'The Watsons Go to Birmingham' helped to shape her appreciation of literature when she was in middle school.

I thought that was cool. We didn't read 'The Watsons Go To Birmingham' or any books of color at my middle school.

I never questioned why we didn't read books written by diverse authors. No. it never occurred to me. I just read what was assigned.

As we talked further about race, Rakiya shared about her ancestry and how her great great grandfather had been a slave in Alabama.

Listening to some of the heart wrenching stories that had been passed down to Kiya made my blood boil. This was not a movie that I was watching. These were real life events that had happened to her ancestors.

It really made a difference to hear about slavery from someone who's famiy had been directly impacted by such an atrocious act.

As I sat there listening to Kiya, I was in awe of her perspective.

I realized that although I was also black and had come from servitude in Ghana, I had a lot to learn about American history, culture and choices.

Kiya was curious about my background too. She had heard that people from Africa were from royalty.

I laughed at that.

Yes, there were royals in Africa. Several of them. But I wasn't a royal. I was a village girl form a polygamous home.

I started to share my preteen and teenage experiences with Kiya.

I told her about my family's communal living situation. I described our compound house, my father's wives and life with my 17 siblings.

She was surprised. She couldn't understand how a driver's mate could have 4 wives.

She thought my dad must have been a hot guy.

We both laughed at that.

When I told Kiya about the first time I used a commode, she opened her eyes in amazement.

She was shocked that I didn't even know how to flush after I'd used the bathroom. She couldn't believe that I had used a pit latrine growing up.

She hadn't even heard about a pit latrine before.

When she found out about my life as a maid in the big city, she couldn't hide her disgust.

She thought that was big time child labor. I agreed.

Sharing my maid experience led to a whole new discussion about tribalism and class barriers in Ghana.

She was surprised to learn that some Southerners were fond of denigrating the people from the Northern part of Ghana.

I explained some of the traits that were associated with the different tribes.

She laughed when I told her that thrifty people were likened to the Kwahus of the Eastern Region.

Her response was that her ancestors might be from that part of Ghana.

When I told her that the Ashantis were considered rich and entrepreneurial. She was like, “wait a minute, I think I’d like to be Ashanti.”

We both started laughing. I was from the Ashanti tribe but I wasn’t rich?

We realized that we had a lot in common and that we both had a deep appreciation for culture and respect.

When I told Kiya how I ended up in America, she was very surprised. She even found it harder to believe that a diplomatic family had brought me to America and placed me in a life of servitude.

She was more shocked when she found out that I wasn’t paid for my services when I moved to New York. And that I had been exploited by my employers. Not to mention , the child labor that I had been subjected to.

Kiya was surprised to learn about the young girls and boys who were living in servitude.

She asked me if I had thought about being a voice for the unheard.

To her surprise, I couldn't answer in the affirmative.

I had accepted the status quo and hadn't even contemplated being an advocate for the unheard.

I mean, that was just the way things were.

It was common practice to find a child working as a street hawker, maid or houseboy in the big cities of Ghana.

As we talked, I realized that Kiya had ignited a fire in me.

Maybe, I could speak up for the voiceless. I did not have to wait for that college degree or financial resources to make a difference.

But how was I going to start?

Who would I talk to?
Who would I partner with?
Who would be willing to listen?

These questions were burning on my mind.

Within a short amount of time at the ice cream shop, we had both learned a lot about this global world.

Although I had been living in America for several years, I was convinced that I needed a friend like Kiya to teach me about black culture within America.

I was loving the discussion. Our conversation was light, yet intense.

In the middle of our deep discussion, Jane and Aviva walked in.

They apologized for being tardy. Their history quiz had taken longer than anticipated.

I smiled.

It didn't even matter that they were late. I was happy for the opportunity to hang out with Kiya.

I may not have had the opportunity to acquire such wealthy information from Kiya if Jane and Aviva had arrived earlier.

Since it was almost time for the event to start, we decided to leave right away.

Before leaving, I made one last effort to convince Kiya to come with us.

To my surprise, she obliged.

As the four of us walked out of Maryland Dairy, laughing at our own jokes, you would have thought that we didn't have a care in the world.

The Grisham event marked the beginning of our friendship.

Same Elephants

HANGING OUT

Same Elephants

HANGING OUT

John Grisham was a great speaker. We couldn't believe that somebody that famous was that down to earth. The best part of the event was the Q & A session.

Not only did the audience want to know about Mr. Grisham's writing process, they also asked him about his real life legal career.

They even asked about his hobbies and how he found a publisher for his books.

After listening to Mr. Grisham's answers, I was more convinced that I was going to be a lawyer one day.

I imagined myself working for a big law firm in either Washington DC or New York.

I didn't know how I was going to pay for law school though.

Maybe I could snag a scholarship?
The wheels were turning.
And so was my imagination.

I imagined myself winning big cases and becoming rich and famous.

It was a good feeling.

I walked out of the auditorium with a sense of purpose. And so did Jane. She was excited about the possibility of embarking on a writing career.

That evening, Jane shared with us that she was either going to be an author, journalist or news anchor.

We were impressed by her conviction.

From our reactions, it seemed that Jane and I were more excited about the event than Aviva and Kiya.

To them, this was just another interesting event. They didn't feel like they had encountered a life changing experience.

Kiya said that she hoped that one day people will fill that auditorium for a writer of color.

We all agreed.

It was time to head home. Since we all lived on the route to Aviva's apartment, we agreed that she'd give us a ride.

I was relieved that I didn't have to take the bus.

As soon as we got in the car, Jane turned on the radio. Aaliyah's Back and Forth was on the air.

"Pick up my girls and hit the party scene, tonight ohh...." Aaliyah's lyrics had us singing out loud.

The song had been a big hit over the summer. It was one of my favorites. I couldn't believe that Aaliyah was 15 years old. That was some talent.

I mean, I was in middle school at that age. I didn't even have the guts to perform in a school program.

Wait a minute, wasn't Jane supposed to move in with Aviva this weekend?

I remembered that the girls had been talking about Jane's upcoming move the day before.

Since Aviva lived in a 2 bedroom apartment, they had decided to move in together to save on rent. Besides, the two of them were always at each other's apartments so it made sense for them to share space.

I offered to help move boxes over the weekend. I thought that if I helped out during the day, I could make it to my evening shift on time. Besides I didn't have any other plans. Bambi was going to be working all day anyway.

When Kiya found out, she offered to help too.

Since we'd never been to Jane's apartment, Aviva suggested that we stop by there to check it out before Saturday's move.

We all agreed. Within 5 minutes, we were in Jane's neighborhood.

As we pulled up into the parking lot, I couldn't hide my surprise. The building looked exclusive. We even needed an access code to enter the premise.

I thought, wow! How could a student be living like this?

The foyer was nicer than the outside. There was a reception area on the ground floor. They even had security guards in the building.

Jane's apartment kind of felt like a hotel.

Since she lived on the second floor, we decided to take the elevator.

It must have been a busy time for residents because we waited for about 6 minutes before the elevator doors opened.

As we were the only 4 waiting, we stepped into the elevator and pressed the 2nd floor button.

Just as the door was closing, I saw a woman rushing toward us with grocery bags. I immediately stuck my hand out to keep the doors open for her.

Luckily, she was able to get on. She said hi and thanks to Jane but did not acknowledge me.

I thought, wasn't I the one who just stuck her hand out for you?

But then hey, I didn't make anything of it.

After all, Jane was the one who lived in the building.

Maybe she said hi to Jane because she was more familiar with her?

Like us, the woman got off on the second floor. We said bye to her and went into Jane's apartment.

It was nice hanging out with the girls.

Although we had intended to have a quick stop at Jane's we ended up staying for much longer.

Whilst Rakiya and Aviva made sandwiches because of their kosher / halal restrictions, Jane and I warmed up the leftover Chinese food.

We ate, played games and talked for over an hour.

I learned a little bit more about my new friends that evening.

Aviva was from a wealthy family and could survive without having to work a day in her life. They lived in an estate in New York and traveled to exotic places throughout the year.

Her family owned hotels, banks and several other businesses. She told us that her parents wanted her to marry some guy named Lionel.

She and Lionel had been friends since childhood. Their families worshipped at the same temple. Like Aviva's family, Lionel's was wealthy and highly respected.

Their marriage was supposed to be a union between the two families.

Although Aviva and Lionel were close, the 2 knew that they could not marry. Lionel was gay but he hadn't come out to his family.

Aviva shared stories of family dinners and how they both dreaded telling their families that a marriage was not going to happen.

Lionel was currently studying at Harvard.

Jane's background was different. Although she had grown up in a Presbyterain household, she decided to become an atheist when she was in high school.

She just couldn't make sense of some of the tragedy in her life. She didn't understand why anybody would believe in a deity. She thought that people gave too much credit to a higher power.

After losing her dad to a vehicular accident when she was 10 years old, her mother received a big settlement from the truck company that killed her dad.

As a result, her mom was able to start a profitable lingerie business.

In the process of building the business, her mom spent many hours away from home. Her absence led to Jane and her brother fending for themselves most of the time.

As their financial situation improved, Jane's brother started using drugs. Jane found him unresponsive in his room one afternoon after school. She was 13.

When her brother wouldn't wake up, Jane called her mom on the phone. She was scared and did not know what to do. Her mom instructed her to call 911.

By the time the ambulance arrived, Jane's brother Bob was gone.

Jane was traumatized. She refused to go to church with her mom or even participate fully in school.

When Jane's mom realized that her daughter was sinking into an abyss, she contacted a therapist. With the therapist's help Jane finally came out of her shell.

The therapist's name was Dr. Hood. She was an African American woman who became a dear friend to Jane's family.

Because of Jane's relationship with Dr. Hood she developed an affinity for diversity and fair treatment.

Jane told us that even though Dr. Hood was her therapist, there were times when she was mistaken for Jane's nanny.

She was like, "what 13 year old needs a nanny anyway?"

Kiya reached out to hug Jane after hearing about her childhood experience.

Wow, I wouldn't have guessed that Jane had lived through that much tragedy. She seemed to be such a happy go lucky kind of person.

All 3 of us hugged Jane. My heart went out to her.

I told the girls about how my cousin Bro. Kwabena had died from a peanut allergy the day I found out that I'd been accepted at Montgomery Community College.

I shared with the group that I'd never really gotten over his death. He had been my only family in America.

That was when Kiya asked about my 'cousin' Bambi. If Bro. Kwabena was my only family, how was I related to Bambi?

I explained to them that Bambi was not from Ghana and that she used to live with us when she was dating Bro. Kwabena.

They were surprised. Since none of them had met Bambi, they just assumed that she was my first cousin.

Well, Bambi might as well be my sister. She was everything to me. She was there for me when I had to escape my abusive marriage. She was at my high school graduation and everything in between. To me, Bambi was family!

After I explained my relationship with Bambi, all eyes were on Kiya to tell us about her background.

Jane initiated that by asking Kiya why she wore a hijab.

Apparently, there were rumors that Kiya wore the hijab because she was married.

Kiya laughed. She knew about the rumors. She said people were always making assumptions about her and her religion.

She explained to us that she made the choice to wear the hijab when she became a teenager.

She wore it to assert her identity and to signal pride for her religion and culture.

She told us that contrary to popular belief, a percentage of black muslims in America were actually born and raised here.

Having grown up in a neighborhood with muslim families in Ash Town, I was quick to support Kiya. I congratulated her for being proud of her culture.

I must confess, it was interesting to learn that wearing the hijab was a choice that she had made.

Although I hadn't thought that Kiya was married I had always thought that the muslim women in Ghana started wearing the hijab when they got married or after their return from the Mecca pilgrimage.

Since moving to America, I had come to understand that there were several cultures that practiced Islam and that I needn't assume that all muslims were supposed to have the same customs.

In one night, we had learned so much about each other and our backgrounds.

It had been a good idea to spend time together that evening.

Before leaving the apartment, Jane showed us the empty brown boxes for the move.

We were ready for Saturday.

THE INCIDENT

Same Elephants

THE INCIDENT

On Friday night, Jane and Aviva realized that their weekend was going to be busier than anticipated. They had entirely forgotten about a Bat Mitzvah that Aviva had committed to and were wondering if we'd like to get started without them or just wait and meet at the apartment in the afternoon.

Kiya thought that it'd be better to go in the afternoon. She felt more comfortable going to the apartment when everybody was there.

Meanwhile, I felt like since I had to get to work by 7pm it'd be better to start packing early.

I explained my situation to Kiya. I didn't mind going early to start packing the items. Getting to the apartment early would help us get a headstart on moving the things into the U-Haul.

Aviva suggested that they could just give us the entry code for the apartment.

Although Kiya was hesitant, I thought it was a good idea. And since she didn't want me to go by myself, she agreed to go with me in the morning.

We arrived at the apartment around 9 a.m. The parking lot was full that morning. When we got to the entrance, there were several people trying to get in.

The folks in front of us had already punched in the entry code so we just followed them inside.

We weren't the only ones who entered without keying in the code.

Since we were guests, Jane reminded us to talk to the guy at the front desk before going upstairs.

When we stopped by the desk, the receptionist was welcoming. He was expecting us. Jane had mentioned our visit before leaving that morning.

After checking in, we headed to the second floor. This time, we used the stairs instead of the elevator.

When we arrived at the door, we pulled out Jane's key from under the floor mat per her instructions.

The door opened at the first try.

We were ready for some packing and heavy lifting.
I was impressed to see that Jane had already labeled the boxes that needed to be moved.

We realized that in order to move faster, we were going to need the doily from the U-Haul.

So, we picked up a few packed boxes, the keys to the U-Haul, and headed back downstairs.

On our way back from picking the doily, I received a phone call from Ghana.

Although Kiya and I were friends, I didn't feel comfortable about her hearing me talk about money issues with my family back home.

I opted to take the stairs instead of the elevator.

Taking the stairs was a nice excuse. Not only was it going to give me a little privacy, but also, I could talk for a little bit longer on the phone.

Ultimately, Kiya got to the apartment before I did.

Since she didn't want to have to get the door for me when I came back up, she decided to prop it open with one of the boxes.

This way, it'd be easy for me to enter the apartment.

Considering that we were in an access code apartment with security guards, she felt it was safe to leave the door propped for a few minutes.

Unbeknownst to us, Jane's neighbor on the other side was suspicious and had been observing us.

She thought we were trespassing so she called security.

As I walked toward the door, I saw two security men coming toward me. They kind of looked like the police. I was wondering where they were headed.

I figured it was none of my business.

To my surprise, they stopped me as I was making my way into the apartment.

Oblivious to what was happening,, I smiled and asked them if they needed help.

They told me to step aside.

What? I didn't understand what was going on. Had something happened to Rakiya?

Out of concern, I yelled for Kiya. Then I asked the men if my friend was okay. Did something happen? I was reminded about how I arrived home to a bunch of policemen the day my cousin died.

Please let Kiya be okay. I thought.

The men did not answer my question. Rather, they wanted to know what I was doing at the apartment.

I explained to them that I was helping my friend move.

Again, I asked if Kiya was okay.

Kiya must have heard me call out her name because she came to the door. Like me, she was baffled.

They asked for my ID.
Wait a minute, why did they need my ID?

I was scared!
I put my hands in my pocket.

And then Kiya told them that my ID was in my jeans pocket.

Why did Kiya have to tell them that my ID was in my pocket?

One of the security guard's hands was close to his belt. Next to his gun.

I started shaking.
I was so thankful that I was no longer illegal.

I pulled out my driver's licence.
The other guy asked Kiya for her ID as well.

She told them that they didn't have the right to ask her for an ID.

Why wouldn't Kiya just give them her ID?

I didn't want her getting into trouble with these security guards.

Suddenly, from the corner of my eye, I saw the woman from the other night.

She was approaching us.

I was kind of relieved because I thought she was coming to our rescue.

To my surprise, she told them that we were trespassing and that she knew the resident of the apartment.

How could she say that? Didn't I just see her the night before?

At this time Kiya had still not produced her ID.

She told the security guard that instead of questioning us, they should verify our identity from the front desk.

I couldn't believe that they didn't even have the decency to ask us our names.

I mean, what were they using our IDs for if they had neglected to ask us our names in the first place?

That was absolutely weird. It was like they believed that we were truly trespassing without verifying or asking us any relevant questions.

Luckily for us, the men acquiesced to Kiya's suggestion and decided to radio the front desk.

That was quick thinking on Kiya's part, I thought.

Since we had checked in with the front desk, it made sense to verify our identity with them.

In the meantime, the woman was calling us thieves. She said we were probably stealing from Jane.

According to her, she had seen us slip through the residents earlier.

She had never seen us at the apartment.

She told the guards that she had been observing us since we came up and that we had started moving stuff from the apartment.

I couldn't believe what was happening. How could such a decently well spoken person hurl unnecessary accusations at us.

Was it even possible for us to be trespassing in such a controlled environment?

The whole scenario sounded like a movie to me.

Well the front desk was going to set the story straight anyways. I thought.

Well, nope, I was wrong.

Unfortunately for us, the front desk could not verify our identity.

The receptionist who we spoke to earlier had been relieved by someone else. The new person couldn't find a note to corroborate our story.

This was getting serious.

The woman insisting that we were trespassers wasn't helping the situation either. She even had the nerve to tell us that we did not 'belong' in the apartment.

The surprising thing was that although she was being racist to our face, the security guards did not reprimand or admonish her.

I couldn't think straight. The guys had guns. This was no time to run my mouth.

Luckily, Kiya was not going to allow them to push us around.

She instructed them to contact the resident (Jane) through the front desk in order to confirm our identities.

She wasn't even going to try calling with her phone. No. She wanted the guards to get the information directly from the receptionists.

After several minutes, the front desk eventually got in touch with Jane.

Oh, that woman's face was so red after our identities were confirmed!

I was thinking - shame on you!

The guards apologized to us and handed my ID back to me.

Meanwhile, the neighbor did not show any remorse.

I will always remember her words.
"You never know with these people."

Yeah, we were 'these people' to her. She had just put us in a box. What did she mean by these people?

There was no doubt in our minds that she had a problem with us because of the color of our skin.

SHOCK

SHOCK

We entered the apartment in a state of shock.

How in the world did this woman that we saw earlier this week start this?

Wasn't I the one who held the elevator door for her?

Did she not see me?

Was she that biased?

We didn't even want to leave the apartment. We decided that we would just stay inside until Jane and Aviva's return.

As we waited for the girls, we wrapped up the silverware, plates and other utensils.

Barely 25 minutes into our wrapping, they walked in.

Aviva was crying.

They were so sorry that we had been treated that way.

Jane wanted us to walk to her neighbor's apartment to confront her.

I didn't think the woman was going to care about a confrontation.

That woman didn't care about Kiya and myself.

I believed with every core of my being that she was racist. As much as she may have convinced herself that she was looking out for Jane, her utterances gave her away.

I didn't understand why she acted that way. In the past few years, I had realized that some people were quick to jump to conclusions about certain races.

Even at school, people assumed that the Asians kids were the smartest.

And then there were those who thought that hearing a family speak spanish probably equated to them being illegal immigrants.

It was getting tiring. Why wouldn't people just see us for who we were?

Students.
Daughters.
Sisters.

Friends.

Yes, I knew that I could be discriminated against because of my accent. Somehow, I even felt that it was okay for people to question my heritage because I sounded different.

As a teenager in New York, people did not like me because I was poor and had a different accent. There were times that I thought the kids didn't want to hang out with me because I was ugly.

To combat my insecurities, I tried to fit in by perfecting my english the best way I could. I believed that getting a good education was going to open doors for me.

But even after bettering myself, I felt like there were times that I was treated as if I wasn't good enough.

That day, Jane's neighbor proved once again, that it really did not matter your level of education or socio-economic background, you could be targeted because of the presumptiveness of your accuser.

Kiya's reaction to the incident also taught me a lesson about my naivety. When I did not find anything

wrong with going to Jane's house by myself, Kiya was more cautious.
When I was ready to pull out my ID from my pocket, Kiya knew that she had to inform them about why I was reaching into my pocket.

Although we had both lived in fear, Kiya was better prepared when it came to protecting one's self during encounters like these.

Kiya hadn't lived anywhere else other than America. She was born here. Her relatives were from here.

Her grandfather grew up in an era where he had to sit at the back of the bus. He worked in the cotton fields of South Carolina where his doctors refused to touch his body during employee physicals.

Kiya had always lived in the knowledge of being black in America.

I had an awakening. I wasn't just a black immigrant from Ghana. I was a black person. It did not matter what I felt inside, or how I sounded like. There were some people who were prepared to see me as a threat just because of the color of my skin.

Same Elephants

THE CONFRONTATION

Same Elephants

THE CONFRONTATION

Somehow Jane managed to convince us to walk across the hall to confront her neighbor.

Having seen Dr. Hood and so many others experience racism, Jane was determined to educate her neighbor about the consequences of her behavior.

Jane pressed the doorbell. We were right behind her.

A woman came to the door. She smiled at Jane as she opened the door.

When she realized that Jane was with us, her smile faded. She did not even offer to have Jane come inside.

"Sally, why did you have to call security on my friends?" Jane asked.

Sally began explaining to Jane how she was protecting her by calling the guards.

She was convinced that we could have been breaking into Jane's apartment and was even willing to call the police to stop us.

She kept referring to the atrocities of black people. It was as if Sally was oblivious to Kiya and myself standing there.

Although Jane told her that her actions were wrong, she was not apologetic. She felt that she had rather done Jane a favor.

There was no need for us to go to her apartment.

Obviously, she had expected a thank you from Jane.

My conclusion? Sally didn't think she had wronged anyone. She was a good person. She was just trying to protect her neighbor from suspicious looking black females.

I shook my head in disbelief.

We left Sally's door without really accomplishing anything.

As we sat back in Jane's apartment, she could not let go of the fact that she had to right this wrong.

Jane wanted people to know that it wasn't fair to stereotype others.

Aviva suggested that they contact a newspaper with the story.

Kiya was against it. She thought that if the girls did that it'd bring more attention to 'us'. She felt that as a muslim, people already saw her as a threat. She just didn't want her name to be out there.

Jane did not agree. She thought that it was important for people to see the goodness in others. And that to fight discrimination and racism, we had to speak up for each other.

By the time I was leaving for work that evening, we had agreed that Jane could write an essay for the student paper without naming the parties.

Same Elephants

THE ESSAY

Same Elephants

THE ESSAY

By Monday, Jane had written an anonymous essay for the student ran Tribune about our encounter.

Reading about the incident was surreal. The essay described the chain of events and ended with a call to action - inviting others to speak up and fight against presumptuous behavior.

I wondered what would have happened if the security guard had decided to pull his gun on us. I could have died. Both of us could have died! Slowly, the tears rolled down my cheeks.

Jane's essay was so important. Her words were teaching people to let go of their prejudice.

By Wednesday, several people on campus had heard about the story. Although Jane did not name the parties involved, people began speculating about the victims.

As the weeks progressed, the Tribune staff started receiving inquiries from journalists about the essay.

All inquiries came back to Jane. She was the editor of the student paper.

Should she respond to the journalists? Did she need to get ahead of the story? Or was it okay to just lay low?

When she asked us, we felt that it was probably better for her to talk to one reputable journalist.

However, we didn't know if it was the right decision. Also, we weren't sure if talking to a journalist meant releasing our names to that journalist.

Since Aviva's dad was connected to a lot of important people, we decided to ask him for advice.

He referred us to Dr. Johnson, a journalism professor and activist in the New York area.

After doing a little bit of research on Dr. Johnson, we decided that it was probably in our best interests to speak to her.

Within 2 hours of emailing Dr. Johnson, she responded. She wanted to talk to Jane about her story.

To our surprise, she was already familiar with the essay.

Wow, news could travel far. How had a student circulated essay made its way to New York?

All 4 of us were present during the phone call.

Dr. Johnson listened to our concerns about remaining anonymous. We were afraid of possible hate crimes or even just losing friends around campus.

Dr. Johnson said losing friends should be the least of our worries. She told us that since Jane had published the essay in the Tribune, it was just a matter of time for people to figure out the true identity of the writer.

Dr. Johnson told us that any good investigative journalist could easily trace the story to us after Jane's identity was revealed.

Since the essay was out, Dr. Johnson wanted us to share our story. She believed that our story could help reignite the younger generations' passion to combat racism and prejudice.

As I listened to Dr. Johnson, I wondered if we should have allowed Jane to publish the essay in the first place.

What if we received backlash after the publication?

I thought about Kiya's concerns and her quest for anonymity.

The decision to respond to the journalist enquiry was probably going to be a turning point in our lives.
To my surprise, Kiya agreed with Dr. Johnson. She was tired of people putting her in a box. She agreed that it was important for us to tell our story.

Having Kiya's blessing was important to Jane.

By the end of the phone call, we decided that it was time for Jane to respond to one of the reputable journalist's emails. We settled on the Baltimore Star.

Same Elephants

THE STAR

Same Elephants

THE STAR

Jane scrolled through her emails. She was looking for Jose Hernandez, the reporter from the Star. For some reason, she couldn't find his email.

Then she remembered, she had forgotten to click on the 'keep as new' tab. She moved into her old mail folder. 10 rows down was the email from Jose. She hit the reply button.

"Thank you for your email. Yes, I would love to talk to you about the essay."

She looked up at us, seeking consent. Rakiya responded, "send."

With that, Jane hit the send button.

Within a few minutes, Jose responded. He wanted to interview Jane for an article in The Star.

Wow, we had no idea that things were going to move that fast.

Within 2 weeks, Jose was ready to publish the essay and interview.

Jane's essay about us was going to be featured in a major newspaper.

We were nervous.

If the student paper essay had gotten as far as New York, how far would an article in the Baltimore Star go?

NEWS

Same Elephants

NEWS

The article came out on a Sunday.

That Sunday, I went to church.

As usual, I sat in the very back. I wanted to get in and out of church.

Nobody had said anything to me that morning so I figured that they did not know about the article.

Besides, I was worshipping all the way in Greenbelt and we didn't have any church members from the Baltimore area.

The praise and worship team was on fire. They played songs like God you are so good and kind.

With the drums and vocals, we were bound to sing and dance.

I loved Sunday mornings. Lately, Sunday was the day that I got to enjoy the Ghanaian culture. I did not want to miss church.

I bought my meat pie, bofrot and kenkey at church. We always had vendors in the parking lot.

My plan was to hit the lot for my usual meat pie selection right after church.

I was already planning my purchase by the time the preaching started.

Pastor's voice boomed across the room.
"Put your hands together for Jesus - Something good is going to happen."

He read the scripture and delved into the preaching. I wasn't really paying attention because I was nervous about the article.

We had planned to go and buy copies that afternoon.

Then, I heard Pastor's voice, "Yes, Sasha, stand up - stand up sister."

Eish, what had I done?
Why was Pastor mentioning my name?

Reluctantly, I got up.

Then Pastor told the congregation to clap for me.

Oh, my, why did I deserve cheers?

Apparently, Pastor had seen the article that morning.

He told the congregation how proud he was of me. And how they needed more of us to speak up for issues that affected our communities.

Everybody was clapping.

Oh my, I wondered what the article had said about me.

I couldn't wait to meet up with Aviva and them.

Since neither of us subscribed to the newspaper, we had to drive to the nearest gas station that carried the Star that afternoon.

I figured there was no way that I could slip out of church.

Pastor was definitely going to want to talk to me.

I knew for a fact that church members would want to congratulate me as well.

As I made my way to the front of the church to greet Pastor, my fellow church members were full of congratulatory messages.

I was being treated like a star. They couldn't wait to read the article and were full of praise for me for standing up for others.

After about 20 minutes of congratulatory messages, I made it to the front of the church. Pastor was all smiles. He asked me to wait for him in his office.

I thought, there goes my meat pie!

It didn't take long for Pastor to make it back to his office. He proceeded to show me the article.

It was on the front page!

Whaat! I thought to myself.

Of all the issues and events, our story was on the front page of the Baltimore Star. This was big.

And it was bound to get attention from others.

Our anonymity was over.

Pastor even offered to give me a ride home. It had been a while since I rode in Pastor's car. Infact, it had been years.

I guess being in the Star warranted VIP treatment.

I accepted the ride.

After Pastor dropped me off, I hailed a cab to Aviva's house.

I couldn't wait to see my friends. I had a lot to tell them.

As I got out of the cab, I saw them.

Aviva and Jane had bags of groceries in their hand. They had just been to the grocery store.

I walked over to help them with the bags.

Like me, they had already heard about the article. They just hadn't seen it yet.

After off loading the groceries, we called Kiya and told her that we were on our way to pick her up.

We wanted to buy copies of the newspaper.

Luckily, we were able to secure copies from a gas station in Columbia. We bought 10 copies and started driving back to Aviva and Jane's apartment.

Although we wanted to get back to the apartment before reading, our anxiety got the better part of us.

We started reading right away.

Because we read out loud, Aviva already knew the story by the time we arrived at the apartment.

As soon as we entered the apartment, Aviva's phone started ringing. Her parents had heard about the article and felt that they needed to retain an attorney for us right away.

Why did we need a lawyer?

Mr. and Mrs. Schwartz thought that things could escalate. Since Jane's old apartment building had been named in the article, they wanted to protect us.

I did not have money to pay a lawyer. Neither did Kiya.

Despite Jane's flashy lifestyle, I doubted that she could retain a lawyer either.

Well, we didn't have to worry, the Schwartz were going to pay for the lawyer's services if needed.

Wow! Our lives were probably about to change.

Same Elephants

THE GATHERING

Same Elephants

THE GATHERING

As I watched the news that evening, I saw the Pinewood Properties sign. Then the anchor began talking about the incident which happened at Pinewood a few weeks ago.

Wait a minute, that was us. Oh my goodness. Had the news media already gone to Jane's old apartment? What was next?

I thought about Sally.
There was no way she was going to be silent about this. She would want to defend herself.

And the security guards? Were they going to lose their jobs?

This was bigger than I had anticipated. I picked up the phone to call Rakiya. She beat me to it.

Kiya's group of friends had decided that it was time to organize a peaceful protest against racism.

She had called to ask if I'd like to join them.

The group was planning to meet at Kiya's apartment to discuss the protest the next evening.

I told them I was in.

I called out to Bambi. I asked her if she'd be interested in the peaceful protest.

Her response?
"Hell yeah."

We both planned on going to Kiya's house for the meeting.

In my excitement, I forgot to mention that I'd seen news about the incident on the news.

As I sat there that night, I began to visualize the atmosphere on campus the next day.

I wasn't sure how things were going to be like so I skipped classes the next day.

I just wasn't confident enough to go to school. I felt that people were going to ask me questions and I just wanted a little bit more time to myself before facing the world.

That Monday evening, Bambi and I went to Kiya's house. Her group of friends were gathered in the living room. It was packed.

Kiya kind of kicked off the meeting by telling everyone why we were there. And then she turned it over to her friend Russell. Russell was going to explain the process and how to create awareness for the protest.

Although Kiya had mentioned Russell, I had never seen him in person.

That day, he was in a white t-shirt and blue jeans.

Although he was talking about serious issues, he had no emotion on his face.

For some reason, I couldn't concentrate on what he was saying. I was just mesmerized by his voice.

Every time he looked up in my direction, my heart did a flip flop.

I couldn't believe it. I had just met the guy. Yet, I had a big crush on him.

Instead of me to focus on the logistics of the protest, I was daydreaming about Russell.

Okay, so what was I going to say to him after the meeting?

Was he even going to stay behind?

This was crazy!

I leaned over to whisper in Bambi's ear - He's so hot!

Bambi giggled.

Russell was methodical in his approach. He explained the reasons why we needed to educate the community and the importance of a non violent protest.

Like me, he had seen the news about the apartments on TV.

Our group was worried about escalated tensions.

Russell and Kiya thought that the best way to combat the tension was to educate the people.

We had to show them that we were decent people who wanted to be treated with respect.

Our goal was to recruit other college students and community activists to join us at Montgomery Park. We scheduled the protest for the upcoming Saturday.

Same Elephants

THAT CRUSH

THAT CRUSH

After the meeting ended, people started leaving Kiya's apartment. There were a few who stayed behind. Russell was one of them.

I saw him talk to Kiya. And then they looked my way. He had that intense look. I wondered what they were talking about. Did he have questions for me?

Lawd, what was he thinking?

I asked Bambi if I should go talk to him. Her response was affirmative.

I gathered the courage to walk into the kitchen where Kiya and Russell were still talking.

He looked up and smiled as I walked in. I melted. Literally melted.

I smiled, stuck out my hand and introduced myself. He took my hand and smiled into my face. "I'm Russell," he said.

As his hand touched mine, I felt some kind of electric current run through my body. I had never felt like that before. I didn't even know that a person could make you feel that way.

I wondered if he had felt that surge as well. I couldn't tell by that smile. He seemed so calm and collected.

He said he'd heard a lot about me from Kee.

Oh, I didn't realize that Kiya had another nickname.

And then his next words had me melting all over again. He said Kee didn't tell him that I was that beautiful.

Whew!
It was getting hot in that room.

Okay, was this guy a player or was he just paying me a compliment?

Whatever he was doing was working. He totally had me at hello.

And if he was our leader, then I was going to work this protest like my life depended on it.

Forget that I was the one who had faced discrimiantion. It didn't matter that the protest was a direct result of an article about me and my friends. I was all in because I wanted to see more of Russell.

He said he was on his way out but would like to get to know me better.

He asked if I had a cell phone.
I said yes.
He asked to see it.

Like a robot, I handed my flip phone over to him.
He put his number in my phone, gave it back to me and said that we should hang out sometime.

I said, sure.

He didn't ask me for my number.
I didn't care.
I knew he would find me.

Same Elephants

THE PROTEST

THE PROTEST

By Friday, we were ready for the protest. Aviva and Jane had also recruited friends to join the group.

It was nice to see a diverse group of people standing together with one voice.

We showed up at Montgomery Park with our signs.

The plan was to start with a few speeches at the park and then head to the streets.

We wanted people to see us. A diverse group of people with one voice. Our unity was the message. That was the way we planned on creating awareness.

This initial protest was going to be the first of many.

We did not realize that word had gotten out about our peaceful protest and that there were others who also wanted to protest against us.

After the initial speeches, we started walking toward the streets.

Unbeknownst to us, the other group was heading in our direction.

The police had also gotten wind of our intentions.

The other group arrived and started shouting at us.
We were determined to be respectful.
We were not going to fight anyone.

I heard some commotion on my far right.
Then I heard screams.
What could be happening?

Somehow, Jane had gotten into an exchange with someone. That person's group tried to fight back. One of our guys decided to stand in front of Jane and Aviva to protect them.

Unfortunately, someone had punched the guy. The guy started bleeding and a fight erupted.

There was a lot of commotion. The police arrived just in time to break up the fight but the guy and a few others were already hurt.

Luckily, an ambulance arrived a few minutes later. The injured were taken to the hospital.

The guy who got hurt as a result of protecting Aviva and Jane was taken to the hospital too.

His name was Asher. He was a senior at Maryland.

We quickly found out where the ambulance was headed and decided to drive there.

Same Elephants

CHANGES

CHANGES

None of us got into trouble with the police for protesting that day.

Luckily, all the injured were treated and eventually discharged from the hospital.

Over the next few months, we participated in protests around the Maryland and DC area.

Contrary to our predictions, our story did not become a national sensation. The news died down after a while.

However, our actions ignited a movement within colleges.

Several students became actively engaged in fighting against racial inequity and injustice. They educated communities about the negative impact of presumptuous behavior.

By speaking up, we had made a difference.

We knew that discrimination was not going to vanish within a matter of weeks, but by educating others, especially, our generation and the younger ones, we could help change the way our society viewed people.

Same Elephants

AFTERMATH

AFTERMATH

Pinewood Properties still stands.

We heard that the security guards were fired and that Sally ended up moving out of town.

Asher and Aviva fell in love and began dating.

After a few dates with Russell, we started going steady. This time, being in a relationship was easy. We seemed to be on the same page. I was looking forward to spending forever with Russell.

However, it wasn't meant to be.

Russell was a senior and was about to graduate. He had several female friends and my experience with Lamar had scarred me.

I did not want to find out that he had betrayed me so I broke it off with him right before his graduation.

He was offered an expatriate job in Ghana and left the country shortly after.

I wondered if things could have been different for Russell and I if he had stayed in the United States.

I even toyed with the idea of moving to Ghana and making a life with him there.

But I wasn't about to give up on my American dream because of a guy.

I decided to focus on my studies so I could land the best internship.

Before long, our senior year came to an end. We graduated and became alumni of the University of Maryland.

We were ready to take on the world!

PART II

NEXT CHAPTER

PSA

PSA

Six years after graduation, Asher and Aviva decided to get married.

Aviva thought it was the perfect opportunity for a reunion.

We were excited, the crew was heading to Maui to celebrate 2 of our favorite people!

Same Elephants

JOURNEY TO REUNION

Same Elephants

JOURNEY TO REUNION

Passenger Sasha Badu to the front desk. Sasha Badu to the front desk.

As I made my way to the terminal, I heard my name on the PA system. I wasn't late for the flight. Why were they calling out my name? Could it be an upgrade? Or maybe they were ready to assign seats to those of us in unassigned seats.

I was hoping that it was the former.

See, although I had purchased a basic economy ticket for an almost sold out flight, I wished that by some mere miracle, I would be bumped to first class. After all, it was my birthday weekend. A girl could dream.

I started doubling up my steps. I wanted to get to the check in counter as fast as I could.

Maybe I could smile my way to a better seat.
I was heading to Maui to meet the squad.

My girl Aviva was getting married to Asher - the love of her life. Asher and Aviva just had that sweet cozy relationship.

We had always known that they'd be one of the long haul relationships.

When I arrived at the counter, I flashed all of my 32 teeth at the service rep.

In my head I was thinking... Jesus, let this woman give me first class la!

Ma'am, I am Sasha Badu, I said politely.

She smiled, typed up something on her screen and handed me my new boarding pass.

I looked at the pass, smiled and thanked her.

In my head, I told myself, Sasha, behave, you are in public. No jumping up and down.

My brain was happy! Seat 3A! I couldn't believe it! First class chic! Walayi!

Yeah baby! I was flying to Maui in style!! The heavens had heard my prayer.

This trip was going to be fantabulous!!

Before long, it was time to board. And you know it. I was boarding group 1. Yeah. That's how first class travels.

This economy traveling girl was rolling with the VIPs!

I wanted to behave like flying first class was my normal.
I took a deep breath, got up slowly and began walking towards the gate confidently.

As I walked to the plane, I felt like I was some rich chic! Here I was, flying first class to a fancy hotel in Maui! Chai, this was the American dream! Live and colored!

Thank you Jesus! I was my relatives' aspirations.

Same Elephants

FIRST CLASS

Same Elephants

FIRST CLASS

Now, let me tell you something. Sasha Badu flying first class is a very big deal. Since my first airplane ride to America from Ghana, I had always sat in an economy seat. I never thought that I'd be able to fly in luxury.

That upgrade was everything.

I did a little head bop at the boarding gate. I was on cloud 9.

The stewardess welcomed me on board. She even helped me put my carry on bag in the overhead compartment.

I didn't have to walk far. 3A was one of the front seats.

It was nice to settle into the big comfy seat. The leg room was massive. I didn't have to worry about the passenger in front of me cramping up my space with a reclined seat. I even had my own TV and headphones for the flight.

It was such a good feeling to be sitting in the first class cabin.

The VIP treatment started before takeoff.

As soon as I sat down, they asked me if I'd prefer wine, juice or water.

Whatt! I had that many options? And I didn't have to pay extra?

You know what I did? Although I didn't drink alcohol, I opted for wine. I just wanted to pose with the drink and take pictures. Yours truly was ready to show off and brag to her peeps.

The boarding process was quicker than expected. Takeoff was easy. I hardly felt it. I wondered if the plane just rode smoother when you were sitting in first class.

As we surged past 10,000 feet, the pilot welcomed us on board and told us to expect a smooth ride.

I pulled out my newly acquired Maya Angelou's "And Still I Rise." As I delved into the poem *Phenomenal Woman*, I truly felt that I deserved to be seen as a phenomenal woman.

Maya's words echoed in my brain -

"I'm a woman

Phenomenally.
Phenomenal woman,
That's me."

I couldn't finish reading though. For some reason my eyes started getting heavy. Maybe it was because I had stayed up to pack my bags.

Before I knew it, I was fast asleep.

However, halfway through the flight, I woke up with a jolt.

In my dreams I had heard a sound. You know that beep when the pilots want to communicate with the crew? Yes, that was it.

I thought the crew was probably going to give us an update. Maybe it was time to eat?

As the stewardess talked on the phone, I started feeling a sense of alarm.

Because I was terrified of flying, I always watched out for body language and signals from the airline crew.

This attendant wasn't good at masking her fears. Her grim face was an indication that she didn't like what she was hearing on the other end of the line.

As soon as she hung up the phone, she reiterated the need for us to keep our seatbelts fastened.

The pilot must have told them not to serve refreshments because they docked the serving carts and immediately strapped themselves into their seats.

When the stewardess puts on her seatbelt mid flight, you know that it's serious business.

My heart started beating fast. What was happening? Where were we? Were we flying over the ocean? Was the plane alright?

The negative scenarios were flooding my thoughts.

Before long, the pilot announced that we were about to encounter severe turbulence.

Oh, how I wished I wasn't on the flight.

I was terrified. I began to sweat in anticipation of the shaking. I started praying and singing at the same time.

I wanted God to forgive me for all my sins, in case we died on the flight.

What if the plane went down amidst the turbulence? How about if we got lost on the radar? I had palpitations. I couldn't breathe right.

And just like that, the shaking began.

I had never experienced that much turbulence on a flight. It felt like I was being pulled from my seat.

Bags were falling out of the overhead compartment. Passengers began to scream. Little kids were crying. It was chaotic. The crew were still seated. Nobody was coming to our rescue.

Amidst the chaos, I felt the plane drop. I was convinced that we were about to crash.

I made peace with my God and prayed that He takes care of my relatives. I thought about Mama and closed my eyes tightly. The worst was about to happen. It was all in God's hands.

I put my head down and prepared for impact. I was wondering if it was going to hurt. Was I going to drown? Was it going to be a quick death? Was the plane going to catch fire?

The thoughts felt like an eternity.

And then I heard clapping.

Did I already die?
What was happening?

I lifted my head and slowly opened my eyes. I was alive. We were still on the plane. It was a miracle.

I turned to the whimper on my left. The passenger next to me had a bruise on her forehead. Somehow, she had hit her head during the turbulence.

The airline attendants were up from their seats, walking through the aisles, helping and comforting patients. A few other people were injured on the flight.

I was lucky. Despite my emotional chaos, I appeared unscathed.

Then we heard the pilot's voice over the PA system.

He assured us that the rest of the plane ride was going to be smooth.

Passengers in the healthcare field were asked to help the injured.
Some passengers were crying, others were comforting each other.

I sat in my seat. Thanking God for delivering me from harm. Promising that I was going to be a good christian going forward. I decided that I would need to take a life insurance policy on myself so that if something happened to me, my family could at least receive that money.

Eventually, the attendants resumed food service on the flight. Most of the people in my cabin were not even interested in the food. Maybe like me, they had lost their appetite.

I just wanted to arrive at my destination. I was already dreading the flight back home. If only, I could drive back from Hawaii!

Then we heard the pilot's voice announcing that we were approaching our final descent into Maui.

What a relief!

I thanked God for keeping me safe. I felt like I had escaped a terrible ordeal.

Same Elephants

MAUI

MAUI

It was a relief to finally land in Maui.

As we prepared to deplane, I realized that there were more injuries on the flight than anticipated.

A few of the injured were taken off the plane for treatment. An EMS crew was at the airport to transport some passengers to the hospital.

Doctors were on hand to check on passengers too.

Like the other uninjured passengers, I responded to questions about my physical condition before deplaning. The airline was probably covering its basis for potential lawsuits.

I wondered if any of the passengers were contemplating suing the airline for injuries.

Me, I was just glad to be alive.

After I picked up my luggage, I followed directions to Hertz for my car rental.

Upon arriving at the counter, I was surprised to see only 3 people waiting in line. How were the other tourists getting to their hotels?

Did I make a mistake by renting a car? Should I have inquired about a hotel shuttle?

I decided to engage in some small talk with the service reps. I wanted to make sure that my decision to rent a car was not an anomaly.

After a few questions, I learned that a lot of the tourists preferred the shuttles that run from Kahului Airport to the hotels. However, since I intended to drive around the island, renting a car wasn't a bad idea.

I settled on a Toyota Corolla.

Shortly after picking up the rental, I began the 34 mile scenic drive to Kaanapali through Lahaina.

Maui was beautiful. Halfway through my drive, I stopped to admire the waves. It was a different vibe.

Although I had been to Chesapeake, Myrtle and Dansoman beaches, Maui seemed different. The green-blue water seemed transparent compared to that of Myrtle. As for the Dansoman beach, it had been my favorite by far. Memories of playing tug of war and eating the best kenkey and fish were always fresh on my mind.

However, despite my fond memories of the Dansoman beach, I had a feeling that Maui was going to be an all-time favorite.

The island looked like a lot of fun. I wondered how the residents stayed away from surfing. Maybe I could learn to surf during my week on the island?

Driving down the meandering roads, I spotted a guy selling coconut. That was good timing. I needed to quench my thirst. The sight of the fresh coconut made me salivate. It was time for a quick stop.

I tried to bargain with the coconut seller. I couldn't believe that one coconut was $8. That was highway robbery! Unfortunately for me, the seller did not reduce the price. He could probably tell that I was a desperate tourist.

Since I was super thirsty, I bought 2.

I handed the island man a $20 bill for my purchase. He gave me $5 in change.

I thanked him for the discount!

And then he offered me a straw.

What? Why was he giving me a straw for the coconut juice?

No way, I just drank directly from the mouth of the coconut.

It felt like old times. My thirst was quenched.

I resumed my scenic drive.

I couldn't help but admire the beauty of the mountains, ocean and vegetation. Maui felt like a different country.

I loved the vacation vibe of the island.

I could envision myself spending hours on the beach.

What a great location for a reunion! I couldn't wait to see my friends at the Ritz Carlton Kapalua! Several of us had traveled to Hawaii for Aviva's wedding.

Same Elephants

THE RITZ

THE RITZ

The golf courses leading up to the hotel looked heavenly. Nothing like I'd ever seen.

Well, other than the ones that I'd seen on TV, I wasn't that familiar with golf courses anyway.

But even the nice ones that I had seen on TV didn't quite compare to what I was experiencing in Maui.

As I pulled up to the big fancy hotel, I was blown away. The sheer magnitude and beauty of the building was beyond my expectations.

I self parked in the nearby lot and walked up to the lobby with my bags.

The bell man wanted to help me with the bags but I didn't take him up on the offer.

I wasn't used to all the extra VIP treatment.

As soon as I walked into the lobby, a nice young man with a tray of drinks, walked up to me and offered me a glass of wine.

I declined the wine and asked for a non-alcoholic option. He immediately pointed to the gentleman standing by the drink table on the other side of the lobby.

I walked over there to pick up a glass of fruit punch.

The backdrop was gorgeous. So what did I do? I asked one of the guests to please take a picture of me posing with the drink in my hand.

When I turned to walk back to the reception, I noticed the stairs that led to the swimming pools. The view from the top was stunning. I couldn't wait to check out the sights!

All the ladies behind the reception counter had some kind of flower in their hair. I guess it was part of the Hawaii vibe. They seemed pleasant. I waited patiently in line for my turn.

"Aloha, Welcome to the Ritz Carlton Kapalua," said the beautiful lady behind the counter. I smiled back at her and said thanks.

She introduced herself as Alana and asked how she could help me. Naturally, I mentioned my name and told her I wanted to check in for my stay. She asked for my ID and began the process.

She informed me that although my room had been prepaid, she was going to need my credit card for incidentals.

As I was handing her my card, she realized that my room was not yet ready.

That was my fault. I had forgotten to add my early arrival to my reservation.

She apologized and offered to hold my suitcase for the next hour until my room was ready. I obliged.

We labelled my suitcase and carry-on for safe keeping. She gave me some claim tags in case I wanted my bags earlier. The plan was to deliver the bags to my room when it became available.

Being free of my luggage, I was ready to explore the grounds.

I walked down to the big balcony to get a better look at the pool. As I looked down at the magnificent view of the ocean and swimming pools, I decided to go down the stairs and explore the pool area.

Same Elephants

THE MEETUP

Same Elephants

THE MEETUP

Then I heard someone scream, Sasha!!

The voice was familiar!

I knew it was my girl Rakiya! I would recognize her distinct voice from 100 miles! That's an exaggeration but you know what I'm saying.

I turned around, felt the happiness begin to build up in my chest. KIYA!!! I screamed!

I run like a little girl who was seeing her best friend after a long summer holiday.

We were squealing! Oh my God, I couldn't believe that I was seeing Kiya after 6 long years!

I had missed my girl and wished that we lived closer to each other.

When we graduated from Maryland, she took the MCAT and headed to Medical school. The last time I saw her was during her white coat ceremony.

That was another fun reunion. After the ceremony, we had lunch with her family and toured the Chicago sites. The Chicago-style hotdogs and deep dish pizza was a hit with the whole crew.

We visited the Sears Tower and the Skydeck. As usual I was terrified because of my fear of heights. The girls picked on me until I went on the ledge. That's another experience for the books!

When we parted ways at the airport, we promised each other that we were going to visit or travel together at least once a year.

Well, life happened. Everybody got busy. But hey, at least we talked on the phone and kept in touch via text messages.

I love Kiya. She was my closest friend from college. Seeing her at the Ritz brought back so many memories.

For some reason, I wasn't thinking about any of the tough times that we had been through.

As we hugged, we started crying. We were emotional. I guess we had missed each other.

We couldn't wait to catch up. It was a good thing that we were going to be roomies in Maui.

Unlike me, Kiya had arrived from the airport via shuttle. Although her flight arrived earlier than mine, it had taken the shuttle a longer time to make it to our hotel because of the other passenger stops.

We realized that we could have planned it better. Kiya should have just waited for me at the airport and we would have driven to the Ritz together.

Well, that was in the past. What mattered was that she had made it to the hotel in one piece!

I couldn't believe it had been that long since I last saw Kiya. She hadn't changed. She was probably exercising everyday like she used to. I couldn't wait to catch up with her.

In the meantime, we asked the receptionists to hold her bags since our room wasn't ready.

That was no problem. The staff promised to deliver the bags to our room whenever it became available.

TO THE POOL

Same Elephants

TO THE POOL

Since we had a little bit of a wait to get to our room, I convinced Kiya to join me in exploring the grounds.

First stop, the pool.

Before we began descending the stairs, we spotted a bar by the pool. As soon as we saw the bar, we looked at each other and said in unison - Jane!

Prior to the trip, Jane had mentioned that she'd be hanging out at the bar by the time we arrived at the hotel.

From where we stood, we could see some bodies on the bar stools but we couldn't really tell if Jane was one of them. We decided to go find our friend.

Jane was very likeable. We liked to refer to her as our famous friend. A journalist in DC, Jane was often on a TV panel discussing issues about race, equality, women empowerment, diversity etc. She had become quite the activist since her college days.

As we were walking toward the bar, we spotted a couple giggling by the pool. The girl's giggles sounded kind of familiar.

Lo and behold! There she was - in her sunny yellow dress and big sunglasses. Just like when we were younger, her short hair was sticking out from her sun hat.

“Jane?” We yelled! Jane looked up from the chaise lounge chair. As soon as she recognized us, she jumped up, “whaatt!’

We started screaming in unison, paused for a brief moment, and then we began squealing all over again.

Once again, we were transported to our undergrad days.

Jane was that friend who taught us how to make homemade daiquiris and pina coladas. She was the life of every party - dancing with her two left feet.

After the initial squeals, she introduced us to her friend Jose.

Wait a minute. Jose Hernandez from the Baltimore Star? This guy was our hero from back in the day. How come Jane never told us that they were dating?

Looked like they had a pretty solid relationship too.

I mean, to travel to Hawaii together? That was a big commitment.

When you start taking exotic vacays with your boo, it takes the relationship to a whole new level.

It wasn't surprising that Jose remembered us. How could he forget about us? Especially if he was dating Jane.

We just didn't quite understand why Jane hadn't told us about her and Jose. Ah well, I figured we were going to find out eventually. Now that we'd seen them together, we could find out the juicy details later.

Then I felt a gentle, yet familiar touch on my shoulder. Whew, the electrical currents sent a shudder through my body.

Oh God, please let it be real. I was praying that I would turn around and look into Russell's eyes.

How I had loved that guy during our undergrad days. God help me.

Back then, I thought he was the finest specimen that God had put on earth. He just had to smile and I would lose my train of thought.

Those months that we dated were some of my best days. I wish I hadn't broken up with him. But then I was young, afraid and really didn't know what I wanted.

And it didn't help that Russell found an expatriate job after graduation. I mean that long distance relationship would probably have been hard to maintain.

Aviva had mentioned that Russell was moving back to the States to work for her dad in the Carolinas.

I knew he was going to be in Maui with us and I had kind of hoped that we could rekindle our relationship. I wasn't sure how that was going to go though.

'Cos I didn't even know if he was seeing anyone. Thinking about the situation made me anxious.

I turned around to see who had tapped me on the shoulder.

Of course it was Russell. I think I knew it in my bones even before turning around.

For a moment I just stood there staring at him.

As I looked into his eyes, I felt butterflies in my stomach! I didn't even know what to say.

My heart was thumping.

Lawd, I had to fake some level of confidence. There was no way I was going to make a fool of myself. I was too old for that kind of childish behavior.

I opened my mouth, but the words wouldn't come. Yah, I was dumbfounded.

And just like always, Kiya came to my rescue.

"Hey Russell, good to see you, she said."
"Hey Kee," he said in that baritone voice of his, as he glanced over at Kiya.

I couldn't believe he was still using his special nickname for her. Were they still in touch? Had Kiya forgotten to mention Russell in our conversations?

Hmmm...

Can you guess what I was doing as I was asking myself these questions?

I was still standing at the same spot, staring at Russell. But this time, I had managed to add a smile to my pose.

Then Kiya pinched me. She was trying to get me out of my stupor!

Like a robot, I tilted my head and then opened my eyes widely.

What's shaking Russell? I said in that fake coy voice that I had been practicing in front of the mirror.

He smiled back at me. And in that familiar voice, he said, "it's all good."

That answer sounded golden to my ears. It was just like how I had imagined it.

Girl sees her ex boyfriend, they look into each other's eyes, their hearts skip a beat... Yeah, I'd been watching too many movies!

After a little small talk, we all walked towards the bar to catch up on life.

Same Elephants

OH YEAH

Same Elephants

OH YEAH

As we sat there laughing and catching up, I looked at my watch. An hour had gone by. Time always flies when you are having a good time. I told the crew that Kiya and I had to go check on our room situation.

We walked back up to the reception area to find out if our room was ready. Sure enough, it was. So we headed upstairs.

Get this! We were on the club level!

All the wedding guests had rooms on the club level.

Not only did we have beautiful views, we also had access to the amenities in the club lounge throughout the day.

I didn't even know that hotels had exclusive lounges where you could eat and relax. What a cool idea I thought.

I wondered if a lounge like that would work in Ghana.

The guests would probably have to pay an arm and a leg for such amenities.

I mean if I had access to a service like that, I wouldn't patronize the hotel restaurants during my stay. With that line of reasoning, it made sense for hotels in certain locations to inflate prices for its club level guests.

Our room was bigger than we anticipated. The linens looked super crisp and the room smelled fresh.

Behind the curtains was a balcony overlooking the ocean. From the corner of the balcony, we could see the famous black rocks that we had read about.

In between our beds, we found a welcome note from Aviva and Asher. They had also left a care package on the desk.

To our surprise, the package contained snacks, cheese, bathrobes, slippers and a few more thoughtful items.

We were super impressed. Even the bathrobes were custom made!

After unpacking, we decided to visit the club lounge.

We were able to gain entry with our room keys.

In addition to the comfy chairs and magnificent views, there was a nice spread of hor d'oeuvres. It was truly a good money saving hangout spot for folks like me.

I made a mental note to make sure I utilized the lounge's amenities throughout our stay.

After hanging out for about 30 minutes, we received a text message summoning the bridal party to the lounge.

Well, that was convenient. We didn't even have to go back to our room.

Within 10 minutes of receiving the message, Jane joined us. Aviva came in like 5 minutes later. She was accompanied by Rachel, her younger sister.

You can imagine the reaction. Another round of squealing! It was such a warm and fuzzy feeling seeing my 3 college friends and Rachel again.

Like us, Rachel attended Maryland. She was a freshman during our senior year.

We spent the next hour catching up and talking about wedding matters.

We laughed about how Aviva had disappointed her parents by opting for a destination wedding and picking a bunch of shiksas for her bridal party.

As we carried on with the conversation, Rachel noticed that it was getting close to dinner time.

The family had made reservations for the bridal party at Merrimans. Word on the street was that it was the best restaurant in Maui.

I had even read somewhere online that their kalua pig and sweet onion quesadilla was to die for!

We decided to head back to our rooms to get ready for the evening festivities. It was going to be a long night.

After dinner, we planned on heading to Paia for some live music and dancing.

I was so looking forward to going to Paia ‘cos I figured that I'd get to hang out with Russell!

As we headed to the room, Rakiya said she had dibs on the bathroom. That was fine with me.

Same Elephants

RETROSPECTION

Same Elephants

RETROSPECTION

Since Kiya decided to take a shower first, I opted for a power nap.

I took my shoes off and hopped on the bed. It was soft and comfortable. I wondered if the mattresses were made by special order.

As I lay there, I began to reminisce about the past. I couldn't believe how far I'd come.

I thought about my humble beginnings in Kumasi. From the days that I was using the pit latrine to my Accra days.

I remembered my days as a maidservant at the Abbans. Thoughts of the taxi ride that I shared with my Mama the first day we arrived in Accra.

My journey from Accra to New York.
My life as a maid in America.

I remembered the cold winter nights when I had to wear layers of clothes in my employer's basement because I didn't have heat.

As a tear formed at the corner of my eye, I remembered the day that I saw my cousin Bro. Kwabena at the African store. The joy and exhilaration.

The blessing of moving to Maryland and starting a new school. I remembered the day that I met Bambi and how she had virtually become my closest family in America.

Then the tears started flowing. The memory of Bro. Kwaben's death was so raw. To date, I couldn't understand why God had to take my family and benefactor away from me in such a cruel way.

Accidentally dying from a peanut allergy?
Why did that happen?

I remembered sitting on that hospital floor, my heart tearing into pieces. Not being able to tell Bro. Kwabena about being accepted into Montgomery Community College.

As the tears rolled down my cheeks, I thought about my high school graduation, my ex husband Lamar, the drama with my green card application and how I freed myself from an abusive situation.

I was appreciative of the people that had been placed along my life's journey.

I couldn't believe that I had my papers now!

My life in America wasn't exactly what I had envisioned. There had been too many curveballs.

However, God had been good to me.

I mean who would have thought that a black immigrant girl who was once a maid would be staying at the Ritz Carlton in Hawaii.

I never thought that I'd know people like Aviva, Jane and Rakiya. And to be friends with them? I counted myself blessed.

As I was deep in thought, I heard Rakiya calling out my name. She wanted me to know that she was done taking a shower.

It felt like I laid on the bed a minute ago. I hadn't even been able to take a nap.

With my tear filled eyes, I got up, and began walking into the bathroom.

"Sasha, are you okay?" Kiya was concerned by the look on my face.

I nodded in the affirmative but my friend knew better.

She stretched out her hands and embraced me. As we stood in a tight embrace, I was reminded of the day we met. One lucky evening in Maryland.

I was blessed to have a friend like Kiya.

REKINDLED LOVE

Same Elephants

REKINDLED LOVE

The rehearsal dinner went off without a hitch. There was a lot of laughter around the table.

Later that evening we went dancing in Paia.

Russell and I reconnected. He still had a soft spot for me. As we danced the night away, I wondered why I broke up with him.

What would have happened if we had stayed together? We may have been the ones getting married.

When the DJ started playing the slow music, I put my head on Russell's shoulder. It was as if time had never passed.

I prayed that we could find a way to make it work.

I thought that maybe it was worth applying to University of South Carolina or North Carolina for grad school.

Maybe Russell and I had a chance at love.

I hoped that I wasn't rushing things.

As Russell pulled me in and held me tighter, I wondered what he was thinking and feeling.

Same Elephants

THE CELEBRATION

Same Elephants

THE CELEBRATION

The next morning, we headed to Aviva's room for a bridal party photoshoot.

Aviva was so considerate. She had flown in a make-up artist to help us get decked up for the events.

We had a shoot in our matching custom made bathrobes.

The photographer captured the intimate moments amongst friends. We laughed, hugged and made promises that we probably couldn't keep.

After the photoshoot, we had a light snack and got dressed for the afternoon nuptials at the manmade gazebo overlooking the ocean and the golf course.

The view was stunning.

Jane, Kiya and myself walked up to join the groomsmen.

We were followed by Rachel.

Then the band changed the song.

They started playing...

Hevenu Shalom Aleichem...

Aviva was a radiant and beautiful bride.

Asher was emotional as he watched Aviva walk up.

As I watched them exchange vows, I looked across at Russell. He was squinting.

The possibilities...

Then I heard the breaking of the glass.

Mazel tov!

I was happy!

Same Elephants

Same Elephants

Glossary

Bofrot - Ghanaian Traditional Doughnut
Charlay - Friend
Chai - Say What?
Eish - What? / Oh Yeah?
Wahala - Trouble
Walayi - This is Hard
Yankey - America

THE STORY BEHIND THE TITLE

When I was a kid, Mama was super strict. She had me cooking, cleaning and going to the market by the time I was 10 years old. Because some of my friends didn't have those chores, I decided to complain about my unfair life.

Mama's response? "Elephant you, elephant them, Different you, different them."
- Meaning, I was different from my friends.

Therefore, when I was choosing a title for this work of fiction, I wanted a title that reflected that we were all the same. Initially, the title of the book was Differences Aside but then I thought it wasn't catchy enough so I decided to go with Same Elephants. I hope you liked the story.

- Marjy Marj

Same Elephants

Also by Marjy Marj

A compelling story about a young girl's will to survive

Same Elephants

Praise for The Shimmigrant

"A page turner."
-Rhonda Rawlings, Summit Media

"A compelling story."
-Oheneyere Gifty Anti, The Standpoint

"Funny and relatable."
-Booktique

"Speaks truth of many real life immigrants
-Greenville Journal

"A thrill to read."
-Writers'Project

"Sure to make you giggle."
-Booknook

Made in the USA
Columbia, SC
12 March 2020